To ____________________

from ____________________

First published in 1992
by Brownsword Books
28 Gay Street, Bath, England

Printed and bound in Great Britain by
William Clowes Limited, Beccles and London

ISBN 1 873615 09 4

The
FOREVER FRIENDS
Christmas Book
of
• friendship •
• By Deborah Jones •

Christmas is only really magical... when shared......

..... with a friend ......

.....it's more fun making footsteps in the snow.....

....Putting candles in
windows which
softly glow..

Across the land,
Christmas bells ring,
We gather together
Sweet carols we sing .....

friends meet from
across the miles....

... Cards arrive to bring
warm smiles .....

Even when friends
are far away.....

...they are sure to be
remembered for this
special day.........

The ties of friendship
are not ropes around....

They are ribbons of Love
in which our hearts are
Bound...........

What could possibly make Christmas more special than a friend........

........like You !!

if Kisses were snowflakes....

...i'd send you a Blizzard!

All i want for
Christmas....

....is a friend like you!